WHAT ABOUT THANKSGIVING

WRITTEN BY TOMMY WATKINS

Halloween had passed, and Thanksgiving was coming.

Everyone in the town started putting up their Christmas lights. Even in the local store, Christmas promotions were out.

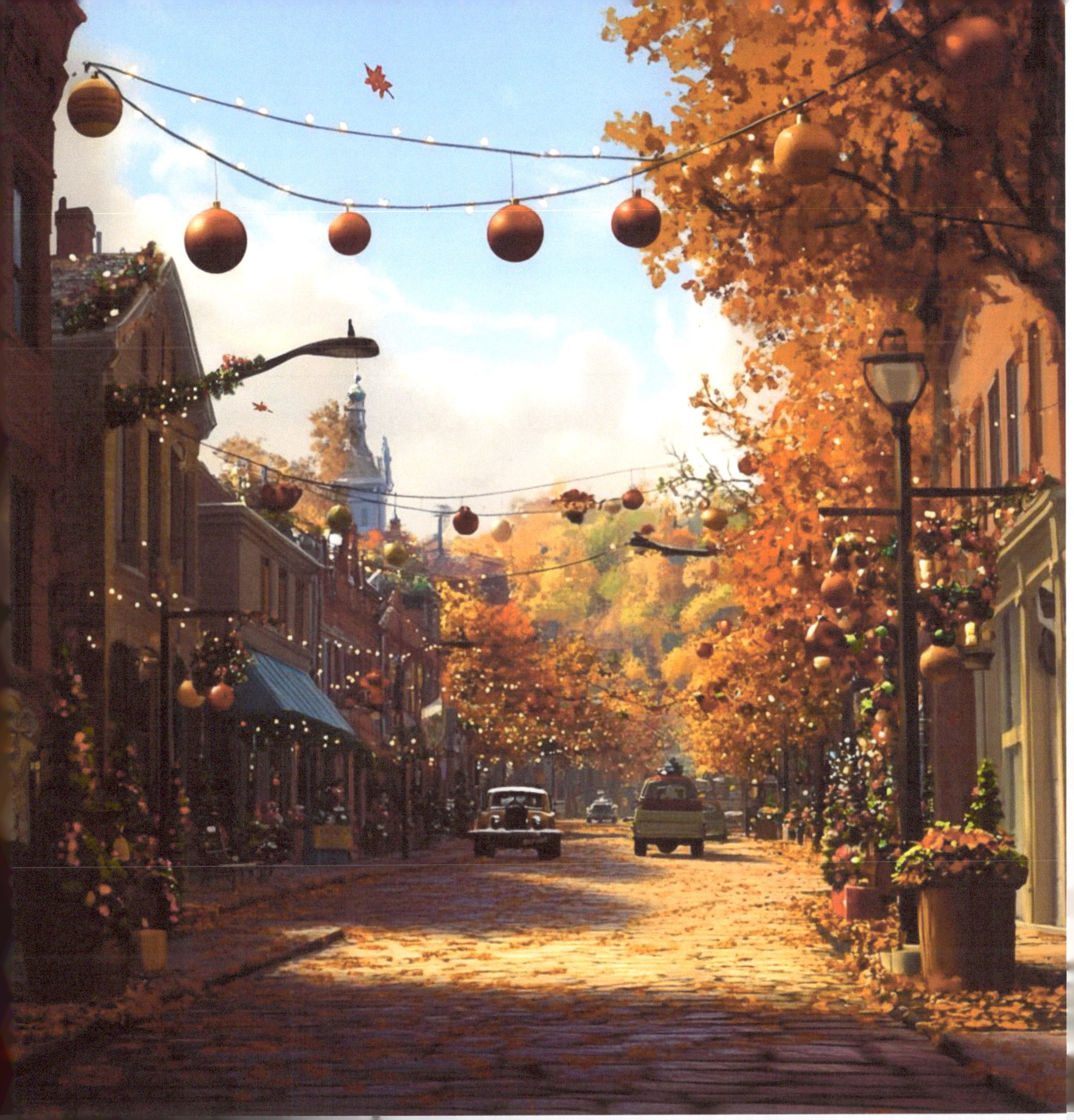

Abby was walking through her town seeing this madness.
What about Thanksgiving?

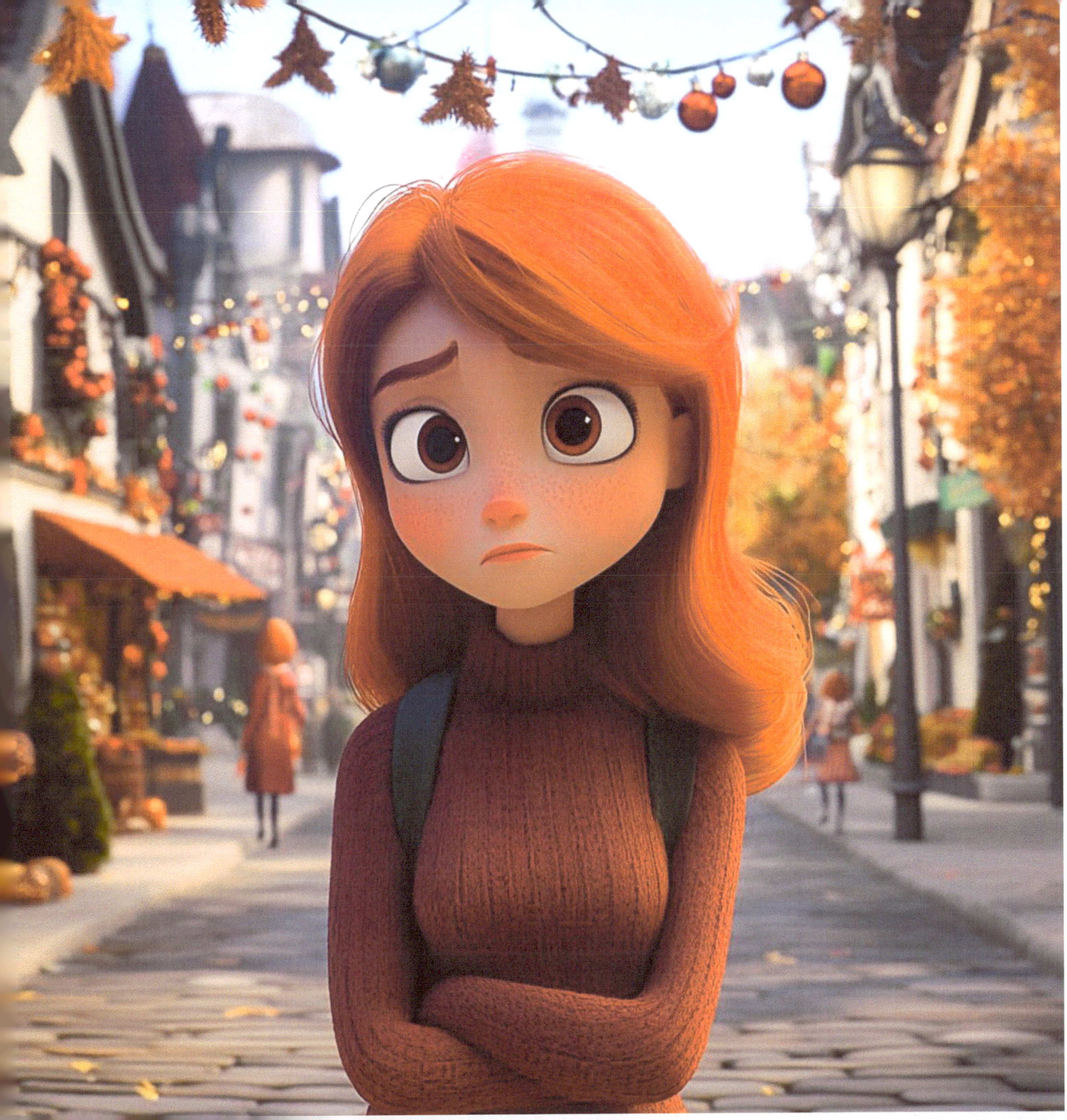

The day would be filled
with platters of delicious food.

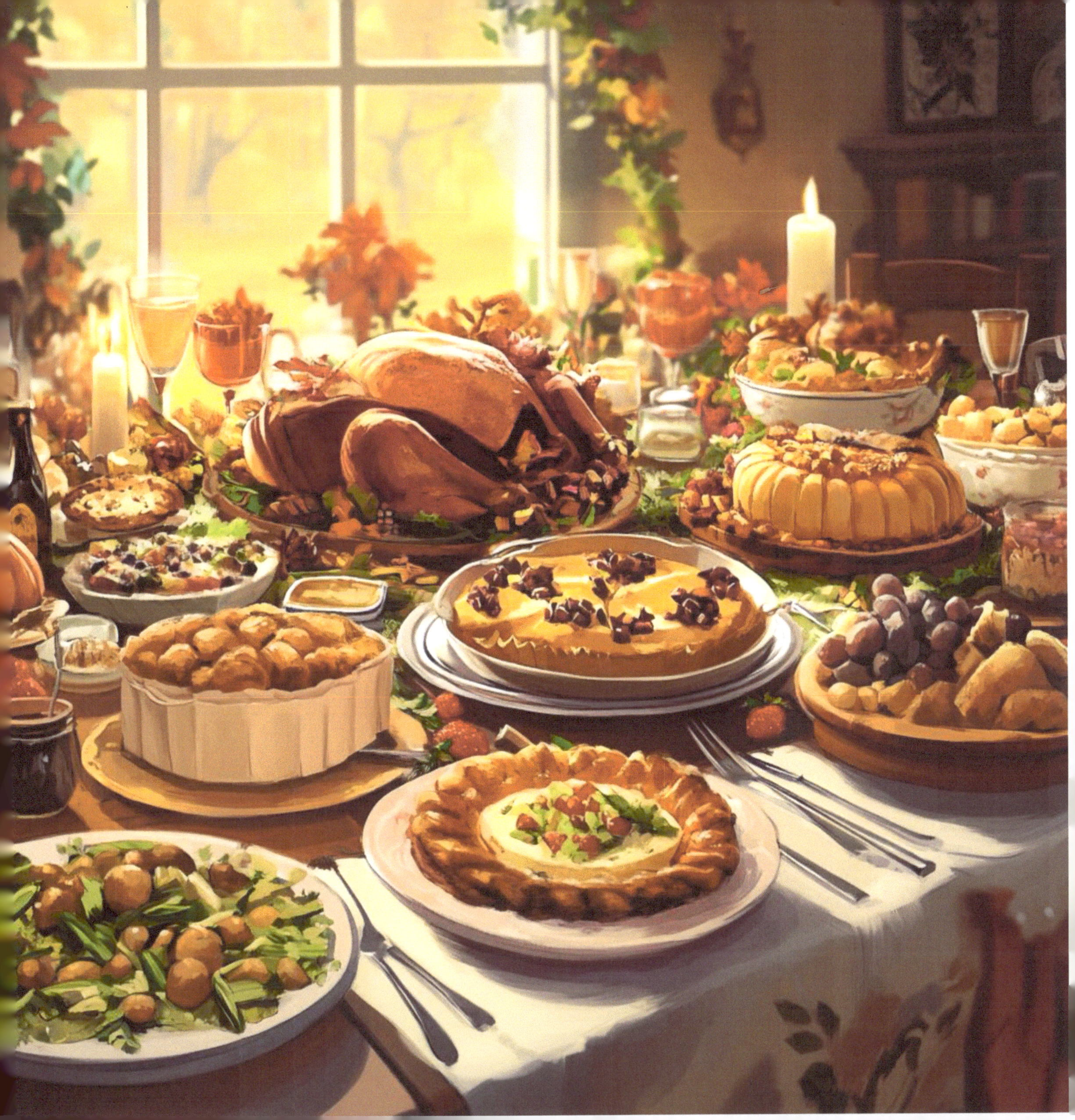

Families gathering together at the dinner table.

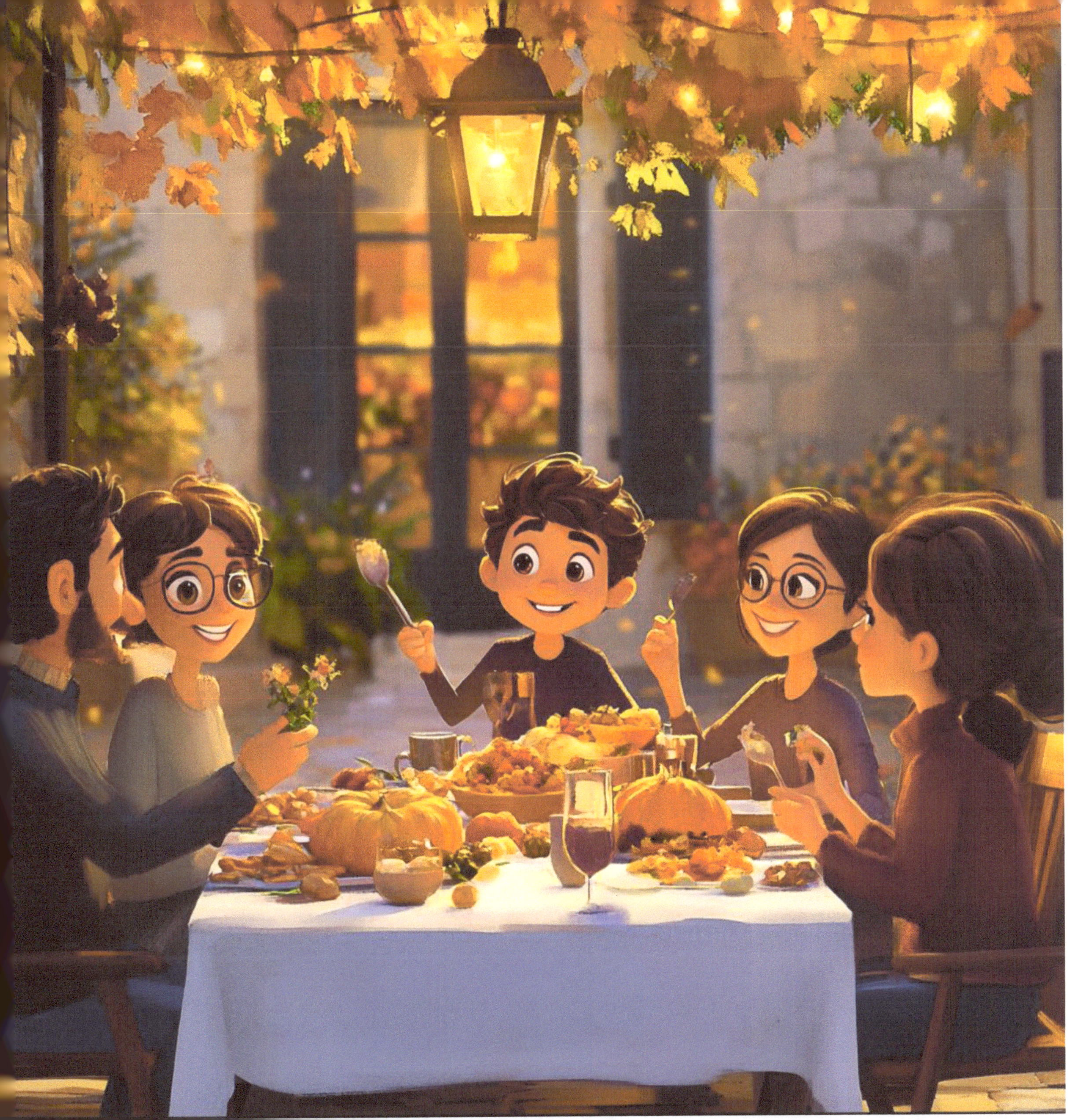

Thanksgiving would be complete
with a football game
playing on the television.

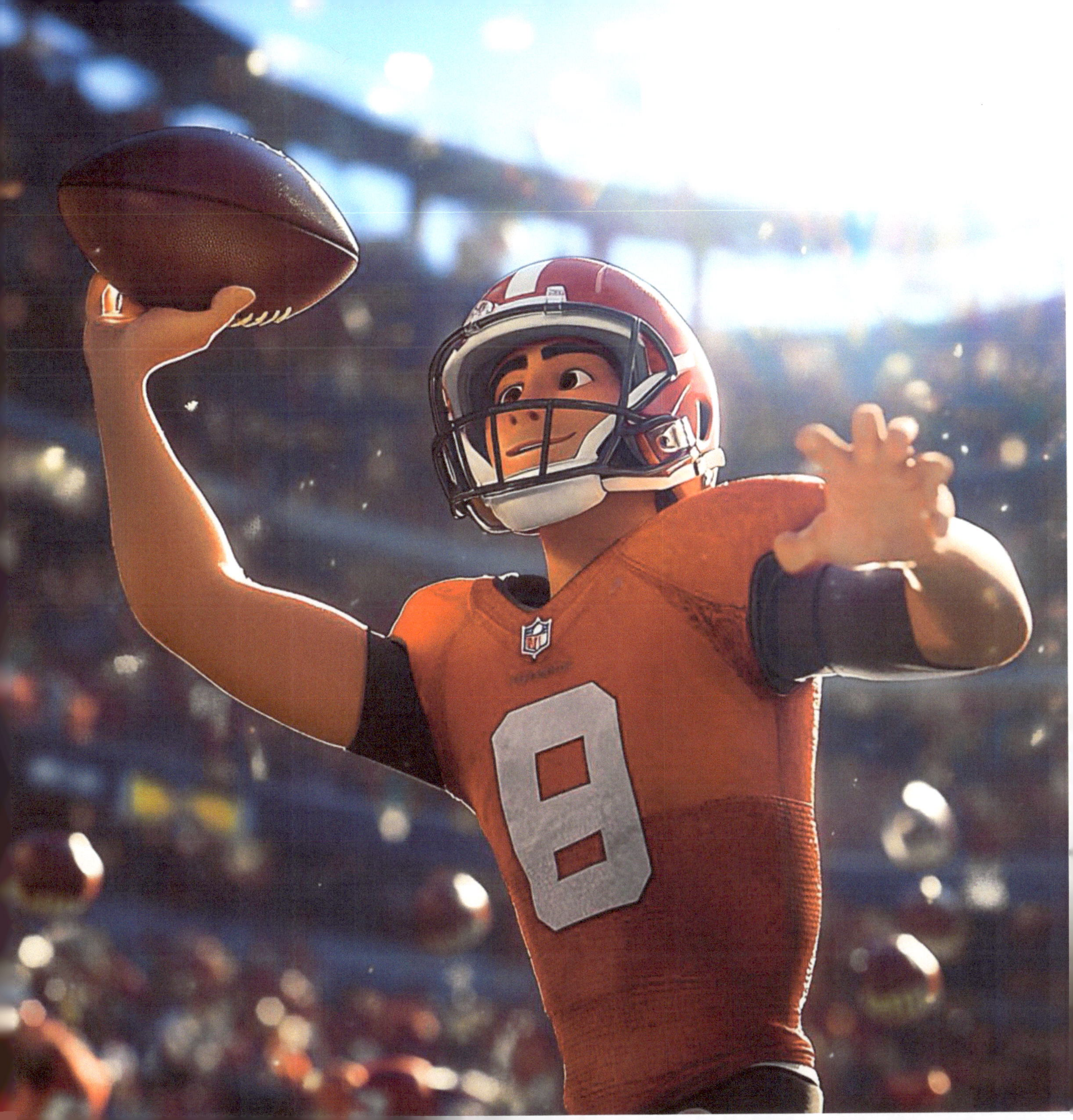

Abby put together a plan to get her fellow townspeople to remember the magic of Thanksgiving.

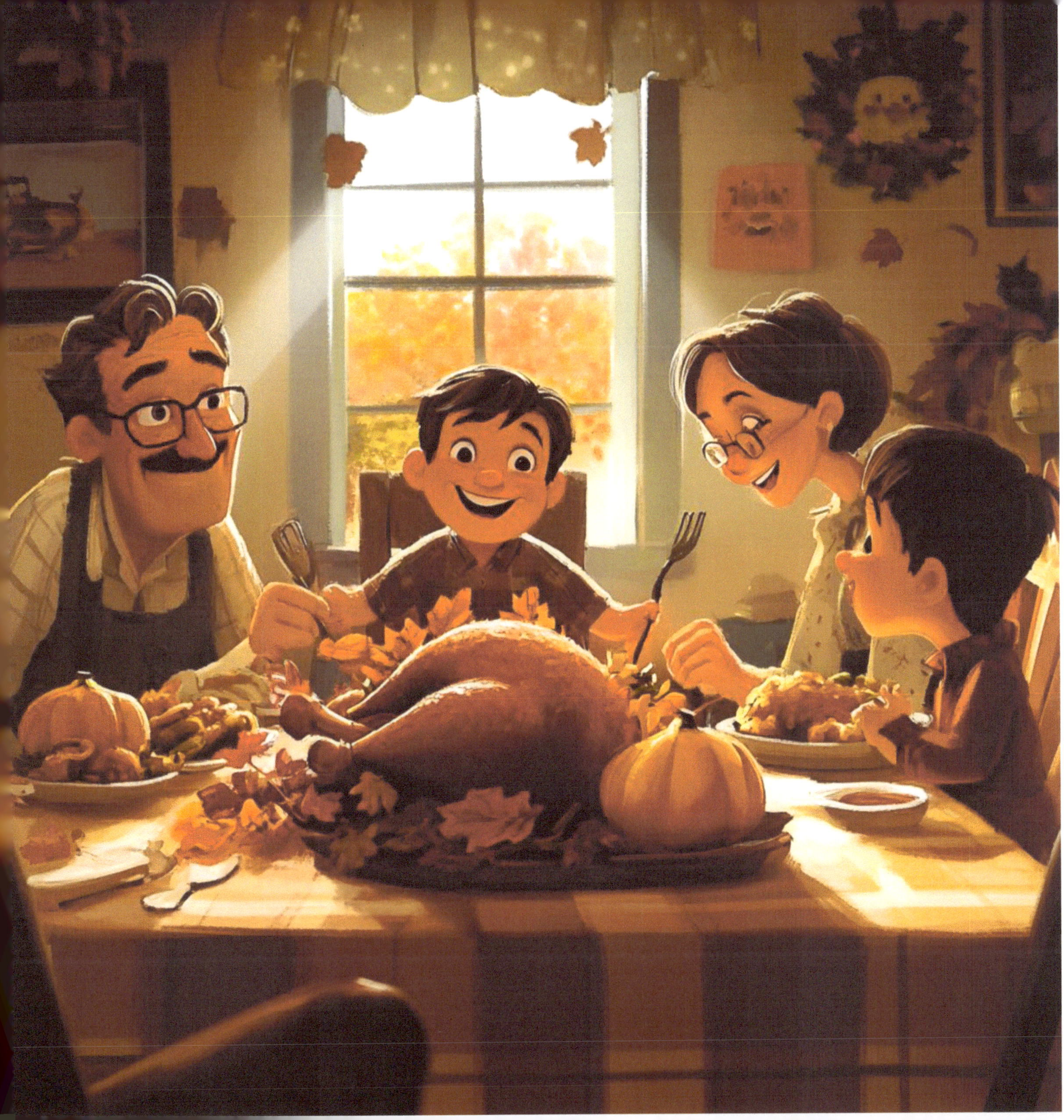

She went to the electronics store to set up a giant projector for the football game. Abby went to the local catering company to provide a Thanksgiving feast.

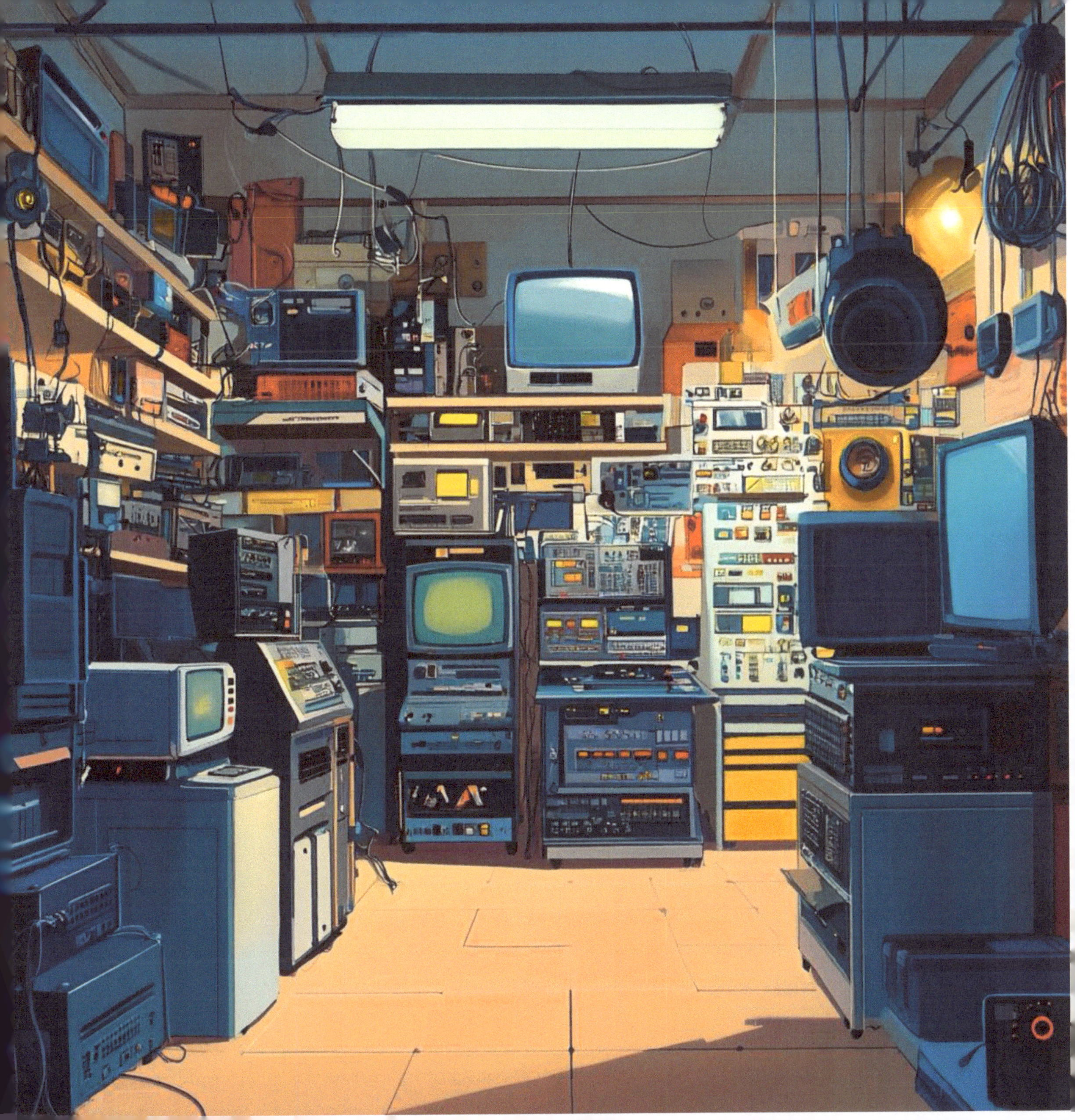

After all the running around,
Abby gathered the townspeople
to enjoy Thanksgiving.
They celebrated and thanked
the girl for reminding
them of the magic of Thanksgiving.

The End